SHEEP

SHEEP

FROM LAMB TO LOOM

for Horton-in-Ribblesdale
C.E. primary School 2009
with good wishes

An illustrated journey by KATE LYNCH

Kate Lynch

First published in 2009 by Furlong Fields Publishing
e *furlong.fields@virgin.net*
Text and Illustrations © Kate Lynch 2009

ISBN 978 0 9544394 2 2

Design and layout by Lyn Davies
Printed and bound by BAS Fine Art Printers, Wiltshire, England

FRONT COVER
Raddled ewes back to pasture, Pitney

HALF-TITLE PAGE
Raddled ewes

TITLE PAGE
John feeds his Exmoor Horn rams

RIGHT
Ewe and lamb, King's Sedgemoor

BACK COVER
Olive Hampton spins wool at the Fleece Fair

Contents

Foreword
Tom Mayberry *Historian*

This beautiful and evocative book captures an aspect of Somerset life which has its roots deep in prehistory. The raising of sheep for wool and food was already well-established in Somerset during the Iron Age over 2,000 years ago, and it is quite likely that throughout the following centuries Somerset sheep were often more numerous than people. When Domesday Book was completed in 1086 sheep were recorded in most Somerset villages, and included 317 at Stratton on the Fosse, 438 at Henstridge, and as many as 800 at Chewton Mendip. By 1900, the county sheep flock was almost half a million strong.

It is unsurprising that the Somerset of popular imagination is chiefly a land of dairy farms and apple orchards. But sheep were always there, quietly grazing the bleak high ground of

The leaping lamb

Mendip and Exmoor, and the more hospitable lowlands of south and central Somerset. In the Middle Ages the Abbot of Glastonbury kept large flocks on manors near the Somerset Levels, his officials carefully noting the theft of wool off the backs of 14 ewes in 1344, and the loss from disease of 367 sheep in 1428. The wool such flocks produced helped sustain Somerset's woollen-cloth industry, a cornerstone of the West Country economy from at least the fourteenth century until the late eighteenth.

Some breeds were characteristic of Somerset. Until the early nineteenth century, sheep of the old Mendip breed, noted for hardiness and a wild look in the eye, were found in 'immense numbers' in the north of the county. They moved between the moors and the hills as the seasons changed, but were gradually replaced by crossbreeds after the upland landscape was transformed by enclosure. In the far west the Porlock breed, 'exceptionally wild and endowed with great leaping powers', long covered the hills around Minehead. And on Exmoor itself, the related Exmoor Horn sheep, noted for the quality of their fleece and meat, still thrive today as they have for centuries.

In words and pictures Kate Lynch brings an ancient story up to date. She travels through the seasons with a small group of Somerset sheep farmers, evoking their lives and work in the county's wonderfully varied landscape – then she follows the related artisans and craftspeople, tracing the story of the sheep and their wool 'From Lamb to Loom'.

Her book celebrates some immemorial patterns of West Country life and is a vivid and lasting record for the future.

Towns and villages featured

Frances Keenan weaves Elsa's fleece mattress on a peg loom

RAMS AND THE AUTUMN RADDLE

The Somerset Levels are thick with an early-morning lilac mist as I leave home. An hour later, further west, Dunster Castle is still in cloud. Then it's bottom gear for the slow climb up Porlock Hill and at the top there's sunshine and the September sky is the colour of a lagoon. There are two ancient-looking horned sheep across the first cattle grid. I'm on Exmoor, Lorna Doone Country, and the tiny lane to Yarner Farm is hemmed with the purples and oranges of heather and bracken.

At least four generations of the Richards family have lived as shepherds and stockmen on this Exmoor coast. 'We're eight hundred feet, rising to a thousand. You've got very shallow soil and it's tough. Exmoor Horns can stand our winters, they've been here for centuries.' John Richards takes me up the lane to a field where seven hefty rams are grazing. 'It's that time of year when we're getting ready for this year's mating. These are shearlings, virgin rams. You'll be alright with them, they're fine for another few weeks, then they'll want to go, they know it's mating time, they've waited eleven months for their month of madness.' He gives them a few nuts as a treat and leaves me in the field. The rams close ranks, butting and nuzzling each other, eyeballing me from time to time. Then they settle back to munching the grass and I get a strong whiff of their rammy scent.

Exmoor Horn rams biding their time

A week later I'm back, this time at Ash Farm. John Richards and his father, Tony, are in the dimly-lit stone barn with five horned rams. 'We bring them in every day around this time to get them used to the halter, it's no good if they don't lead out well. It's coming up to the Blackmoor Gate Ram Sale, it's happened out there so long as people can remember. I'm hoping for a few rosettes. This is an old boy, full mouth, he's five and a half, we've used him three times. If you're not careful he'd be coming back on his own daughters, that's why we're selling him. We all go to other flockmasters to get fresh blood.'

John detects a slight limp in a younger ram, takes him into the yard, flips over eighty kilos of virile animal and digs out a stone from his hoof. Back in the barn Tony is combing their best ram. 'Each Exmoor Horn might look the same, but some have soft wool, some more open, this one's got good thick wool, and the skin's a cherry colour, a nice deep red. You don't want a ram with open wool - when it pours with rain the water goes into the skin - but then you mustn't go too tight with the wool either. Then with the breeding you don't want to breed too close, we select the ewes out of the flock to go with that particular ram.'

It's that time of year, shepherds are sifting and sorting their stock before putting the rams on.

John and Tony with their Exmoor Horn rams

It's the first week in October and mating time at Manor Farm. We are towing six rams down the ridge onto the Somerset Levels – four Texels, one Charolais and one Rouge l'Ouest. At the foot of the hill it's dead flat and we turn off the road along a rutted drove, then another, bumping through deeper and deeper black puddles. This is Huish Moor, on King's Sedgemoor, between the ridge of High Ham and the Polden Hills, one of the lowest and wettest landscapes in the British Isles, a soft peat floodplain only inches above sea level. There's no sound of traffic and not a house in sight. We're in between heavy autumn squalls, there's a vast pigeon-grey sky, shafts of lemon light, rich viridian and green oxide in the grass, and ochre sheep in the distance.

I'm with John Vigar, his father Henry and their shepherd Andrew. It's time to mix the raddle. I'd imagined there might be a barrel of the stuff, with the farmer red as Thomas Hardy's reddleman , but Andrew mixes only a paint-pot full, one spoonful of the earth-red pigment for each ram, stirring it into a thick impasto with linseed oil.

It takes the manpower of all three men to take out one of the Texels from the trailer and keep the brute force of the other rams back. With one arm under its neck and the other hugging its lower body, Andrew lifts and flips the ram. Perhaps just a tad of showmanship. The viscous paint is smeared onto its brisket. One spatula, and another. The ram is stood back on his feet and shoved in the direction of the two hundred Suffolk Cross ewes on the far side of the field. Then the next Texel is manhandled from the trailer.

John and Andrew raddling the Texel ram

The second ram is painted and ambles off in the direction of the ewes. And in the distance there's no mistaking two dark red gashes – the first ram has done his business, twice.

John explains. 'In the old days they often put the rams in with the ewes with no colour first, then sixteen days later they put the red stain on, then sixteen days later, soot. The ewes come into season for just twenty four hours every seventeen or eighteen days and the ram will only serve the ewe on that day. And when she is served she's stained with the colour from the ram's chest. Because a ram won't serve a pregnant ewe, those not red were probably pregnant the first time, then those with red bottoms would be due sixteen days later and those marked black would be due sixteen days after that. In that way the shepherd knew when the ewes would lamb, when to bring them in. It's still much the same today, except we usually start off with the red at the beginning, then we go to blue, then green.'

The third ram painted is more interested in eating, meandering nonchalantly over towards the ewes. Not so the fourth, who fair gallops across the field and head-butts a ram astride a ewe. 'There's always one!' says Andrew.

Then we head back down the drove with the remaining two rams. These are painted and released with a flock of the Vigars' black-faced Suffolk Cross ewes who are in Tapskitt Field on Ham Moor. 'I always think the year starts in October when we put the rams in,' John tells me as we climb back up the ridge to the farm. 'Do you want to come maggotting with us – we're off to the field near the windmill next.'

The raddled ram, King's Sedgemoor

GLEBE FARM, PITNEY

Rob Walrond runs a mixed organic farm and farm shop on the slopes just above Langport and the Somerset Levels. Today he is changing the crayons in his rams' harnesses. It's a grey day, heavy with cloud. Sketchbook ditched, I am put to work as a living fence, arms waving, as a hundred woolly ewes and two rams trot seamlessly from their field across the road into the farmyard, chasing Rob's bucket-rattle of food. 'We use harnesses and crayons, we don't use the paint. It suits us. We start with the lighter colours, stronger later. You can see some have been served, they're green.' Rob is in the pen, thigh-deep in fidgetty sheep. He is all-purpose as he singles out the ram and grapples him. One moment the ram has balls, burly and strong, the next he is belly-up, nestling like a lamb between Rob's legs. The new cake of red is fitted into the harness and the straps tightened. 'He's been a busy lad, but he's all ready for more action. Some are skin and bone after a few weeks' raddling.'

The October sun is sinking and there's a light drizzle as the flock is returned to pasture. The ram idly sniffs a ewe's bottom. In the damp field there's the autumn rustle of brown and yellow leaves. The sheep are all bleached greens and dirty creams, just the ram's red raddle startlingly bright and out of keeping.

Rob catching the ram

Two weeks later Rob swops the rams over, putting them with other ewes. 'Gives them a bit of variety – makes the most of every chance we've got.' This is a palaver and wonderful in the bright sunshine. We herd two flocks home from their different pastures, one some distance away. They are kept apart and rams isolated. Hooves are manicured. 'This Suffolk's had a bit of foot rot, I've opened it up so the air can get to it.' Then the rams are upturned and raddles replaced, this time with cakes of blue. I scribble disjointedly in my book, half-baked figures with sheep. Then, later, we block exit routes as the two flocks are moved back to grass with their new studs. 'The rams won't have much to do now, the ewes are mostly in lamb.'

Sitting in the field, the day closing in, the Suffolk ram noses the undyed rear-end of a woolly ewe. It is a quarter past four. The light dims, colours lose themselves, but there's still a strong purple on the horizon and the sheep are little luminous patches on a grey-green canvas.

Rob checks the ram's raddle harness

GLEBE FARM, PITNEY

November, the end of the mating season. One flock is shepherd-ed back to the farm. Penned in, the ewes are channelled through the race where Rob feels their udders and bares their teeth. The rams are redundant till next season, but eight or ten ewes are redundant full stop: they are barren, have a lump in their udders or a broken mouth and their life is over. 'Not too bad this year, pretty good, only eight or ten killers.'

Then the pregnant ewes are off again, back to pasture, but without the rams. There are three of us, Rob, Phil and myself. We drive them a mile or so, the lane a river of sheep, multi-coloured bottoms bobbing, and there's just a pair of jeans that smacks of the twenty-first century. We could be now or way back when. Phil bounds along the grassy verge, his stick flying. He shoos on those sheep which stop and nibble or gallops ahead to block a driveway, racing to beat the sheep. Rob's head is a tiny blob way in front, and the river of sheep funnels into a dot which is the bucket of food he holds.

We leave the gestating ewes in the setting sun in a tasty field of turnips and Rob looks pleased. 'It goes quiet now till lambing time.'

Raddled ewes back to pasture, Pitney

LAMBING

It is seven o'clock and a raw February night. The Walronds' barn is full of quiet lamb bleet, mothers' milk and full-term ewes. In the yellow light in the corner a ewe is rocking. She has a pretty eggshell-white face and hugs the wall. Now she turns her head round towards her bottom, as if a little puzzled, paws at the straw and flicks her tail very fast. She butts the other sheep away and largely they respect her space. The birth, when it comes, is unceremonious: the lamb slips out, the bag breaks and the sodden newborn is licked curly, dry and clean.

Rob comes over from the house. 'February is our busiest month. It's a dry shallow soil up here, so we try to lamb early and finish them before we suffer with lack of grass in July. The Mules are very good mothers, if times are hard they tend to look after their lambs more than themselves. A lot of shepherding is down to observation, knowing the signals, when a ewe's about to start giving birth, there are lots of signs, like lying down and the head going up in the air, and sort of baring their teeth, when the top lip comes back, and nibbling at imaginary things, all sorts of subtle signs, and when you've got a measure of how long that's been happening you know whether you need to go and assist. We lambed in the fields when I was young, went round late at night with a torch, it's much easier with them indoors. We just didn't have a barn spare then.'

Rob and Jess with armfuls of lambs

Valentine's Day. A ewe has been urging for some time, it may be a breach. Rob is up to his elbow inside. He pulls himself out and a slimy black lamb follows. 'I just had to separate the head and the feet, they were together, not difficult. It's a big lamb.' His daughter, Jess, places it on the straw under its mother's nose and mum begins to lick. 'When the lambs are newly born it's the licking, nature's way, gets the lamb's lungs going.'

Meanwhile Rob is trying in vain to turn the lamb inside another ewe. 'When a lamb's backwards it's touch and go, the lungs get squeezed. This one's too big to turn.' Rob braces himself and pulls. It takes some doing. The lifeless lamb is delivered back to front and Jess urgently tickles its nose with a spike of straw. Then Rob picks up the lamb and swings it like a pendulum. 'It seems a shocking thing to do, but it gets rid of the mucus.'

It's no good, the lamb doesn't make it. There's a palpable sense of loss. The bereaved mother wanders off. 'It's never a good sign, but she's got plenty of milk, we'll put another lamb on her. I've got two lambs on the bottle, twins, their mother lost her milk.' And so a living lamb is smeared with the dead, and successfully re-mothered.

Rob and Jess lambing

MANOR FARM, HIGH HAM

It is twilight the following evening. I am wearing my walking
boots. John Vigar looks at them, shaking his head, 'I'll lend you
some wellingtons. Are you absolutely sure you're not pregnant?'
We laugh. The expectant ewes are indoors, in the middle of
the barn. The new mothers and their lambs are penned around
the perimeter. Andrew is forking hay. John's wife, Jane, is delivering a lamb. 'I'm just pulling the feet out, it's head-first,' she
whispers. 'Can you see its nose? Look, here are its front feet
and tucked between you can just see its little nose,' and then
she eases out the slimy wet lamb and lays it gently on the straw.
The ewe begins the lick, drinking up the afterbirth goo, and
Jane helps, wiping the thick mucus from the lamb's face with
her fingers and the lamb snuffles as if coming to after drowning.
Then Jane is delivering the second lamb. Within five minutes
the twins are wearing smart bouclé coats, at odds with their
bloody noses, and within ten minutes they are gamely standing
and collapsing, as if trying to get home after a heavy night out.

The day is done, cool evening greys outside, but, in here,
warm electricity bounces gold and ochre from straw and fleeces.

Jane delivers the twin

MANOR FARM, HIGH HAM

There's no rest at the weekend. Last night Jane was in the lambing shed till half past nine, then John took over till eleven, snatched some sleep till four and was back in the barn till six this morning. 'I didn't stop, twelve ewes lambed in two hours, some needed help, some had triplets and it's best then if you set the third lamb to another ewe who has lost her lambs or only has one. If you aren't around and several ewes lamb then they may only claim one of their lambs and then there's a fine old confusion of unwanted lambs.'

Lambing is a family affair. John's sister, Mary, has come up to help. She and her husband have the local butchers shop. Mary is crouched in a pen milking a ewe. 'She's got one huge teat and it's too big for the lamb to suckle, it's colostrum, look, it's sticky,' and she holds out her hand, dripping with the thick milky syrup. She gently lathers the swollen teat and trickles the milk into the mouth of the lamb. 'If we leave them to their own devices, both lambs will suck on the smaller one, we have to get this other teat going.'

Henry watches Mary in the pen

MANOR FARM, HIGH HAM

The rain stops as I arrive at the farm two days later and set up
to paint in the corner of the shed where a Scotch Halfbred is
mothering two lambs. She is uneasy and I move further back.
John looks in. 'We've got the ewes in all day today, usually
they'd be back out in the field, but it's too wet, no good if they
lamb in the rain. Six lambed last night, I was out here at half
past eleven, slept till half past two, woke up and came out,
then was back out here again at five. It was lucky, this one had
her lamb's head out, they can't push them out without at least
one leg in front. The lamb would have died and the next would
have drowned behind the first.'

The smell in here is delicious, the air is an earthy soup –
a heady mix of straw, warm wool, sweet molasses and musky
animal. Light pours in from the open side of the barn, painting the
dusky wool of these large expectant mothers a soft grey-blue.
Everywhere there is a dull and steady munching and the odd
mew from a newborn lamb.

Scotch Halfbred with her twins

It is a bright warm day, full of late February sunshine, and there are flocks of starlings wheeling in the sky. John's in the yard and Andrew is about to set off in the Landrover, trailer attached. I climb in and we rattle down the hill onto the Levels and stop at the gate to a field. Andrew opens up the trailer and gently picks up two lambs by their front legs. He is making little throaty bleeting sounds and the lambs dangle oddly. He holds the lambs low and close to their mother and he walks very slowly, bleeting all the time, tailed by the ewe.

Then, in the field, he lays the lambs on the grass and when he is sure the ewe is mothering them, returns for the next. This lamb's wool is crusty and egg-yolk yellow. 'She only had her lamb this morning but it's a fine day and the sun will do them good.' Another ewe comes over from the far side of the field and noses the lamb, keen to mother it. Andrew shoos her off. 'She's got two of her own, it happens quite often. These are hoggs, it's their first time, they get confused and sometimes poach the new lambs. They'll be better next year, second time around.'

Andrew takes lambs out to pasture

Still a week to go before the clocks go forward. It's teatime and the day is closing in. John hails a cheery hello. Penned in the shadows is a ewe drinking up the birthing slime from her baby. 'There's another one coming, but not quite yet. I'm glad you weren't here last night, we had a difficult one and lost the lamb.' Another ewe is bawling and John catches her. 'She's been too long.' He delivers the lamb and another ewe muscles in. John nudges her off. 'She hasn't lambed yet, if she licks this one for too long she won't have her own, there's a lot of mis-mothering with sheep.'

There must be thirty pregnant ewes indoors and another fifteen with their lambs, but there's a strong and fulsome silence. 'Thing is, we want it quiet at lambing time, it'll be a bit noisier in three weeks when we bring them all in for dagging.'

A patch of matted straw is stained wine-red from an after-birth and the latest newborn is flexing its legs. 'Ten minutes and a lamb is up on its feet, twenty minutes it's suckling, two hours and it can outrun a man.'

We walk across to the other barn. It is full of straw light and gold from the setting sun. The ewes are cleaner in here, twitchy and uneasy. One ewe is particularly restless, a water bag hanging from her bottom. 'They can have a few of those, it could be another two hours yet. This lot have only been in for two nights, they're not so used to us. We're on the home run now, six hundred and twenty ewes lambed, two hundred left. Soon be time to get a full night's sleep again.'

The lambing shed, High Ham

April Fool's Day. Eight hundred feet rising to a thousand above the Bristol Channel. The blue sky washes into the grey-and-silver-flecked sea below and there's a bitter Atlantic wind. Spring comes later here on Exmoor and lambing has only just begun.

John Richards is in the shed. 'It's good to have the sun today, it was rough old weather on Sunday, driving rain. We were all out, tucking new lambs into their mothers and pushing mothers into the lea of the hedges. New lambs don't know to look for shelter and mum doesn't need it herself. This is when the lambs can die. We lost one. But worse, there's a fox. It's taken one lamb a night the last few nights, just taking their heads, probably a vixen. She's going for the twins, she knows the ewe can't so easily defend both lambs. It's frustrating, there are plenty of pheasants and rabbits about. Hasn't been as bad as this in a long time.'

The air in the shed is laced with the soft lowing of cattle, the odd mew from a lamb and the purr of a quad bike. A teenage niece bottle-feeds a lamb whose mother is low on milk, and a cousin, Ricky, has his hand in the tight cervix of an Exmoor Horn ewe. He pulls out the lamb and gives it a little slap. It is big and bloody. Then he slips back inside and pulls out its even bigger brother or sister. Two more healthy lambs.

I walk away from the farm along a track, becalmed between two towering hedges, to a field they call Higher Ground. Here, in the fierce wind and sunshine and sea air, a flock of good Exmoor Horn mothers are keeping beady eyes on their very exuberant Mule lambs.

Exmoor Horn mother watches her Mule lambs

SUMMER SHEARING AND THE WOOL

The shearing team arrives in High Ham on a blustery May day and John Vigar has a worried eye on the sky. Shearing will be hampered if it rains and damp wool has very little value. Inside the barn the lambs are separated from their mothers and they bawl, then afterwards, when the ewes are shorn, when they are pairing up again, there are cries of loss and recognition. The upshot is there's an unholy din of sheep wailing as well as the persistent electric whirr from two shearing combs and it's taking the men just one and three quarter minutes to shear each sheep.

Dave Takle, an Exmoor shepherd, is running two shearing teams in the West Country this season. 'I learnt how to shear when I was quite young, and when I was eighteen I went shearing in New Zealand. It's a short season over here, just as you get used to it and your back stops hurting and you're fit, shearing ends, so it's great to continue and do some seasons over there as well, it's a good way of learning. For fourteen years I never saw a winter, I was doing the circuit, shearing in summers all over the world.'

I've held him up for long enough. He is tying today, clearing the fleeces as soon as they are off the sheep, rolling and packing them in tough milky-white sheets, twenty-five or thirty to each one. He laces and ties up a full sheet and hauls it into the adjacent barn, where these giant sheepy parcels of wool lie like sleeping animals in the shadows.

Shearing at Manor Farm

40

Jane brings in a pot of tea and work stops. Neil is down from Oban in Scotland and Adrian is a New Zealander, both in the West Country for the summer shearing season. Adrian has a sheepy bleached strip mown through his jet black hair. 'I've been shearing for nineteen years, it gets in your blood. If I'm not shearing two hundred a day then I'd be disappointed. It's my sixth year over here. I don't use a harness, it's quite hard physically, but it depends on how you do it, I try to minimise the energy, try to relax, and I think a sheep senses that. It's like any animal, if you force it to do something it's not going to like it, so try to get as relaxed as you can.'

'Down in New Zealand shearing's quite a profession, it's a sport as well. I've shorn sheep for New Zealand, represented New Zealand against the Australians. People don't understand the pain side of it when you're bending over, it's because your muscles are shorter than mine, down my back, but after a week or so there's no actual pain at all, 'cos your muscles are stretched out. Technique's got a lot to do with it, with a sheep you notice the way I get it out, it uses its feet, so I'm not lifting any weight, it actually seems harder than it is, if it's done properly, and it has to be that way for people to be able to shear seven hundred, eight hundred, nine hundred in a day. I've seen a lot of the world, and I've got shearing to thank for that.'

He sparks up a cigarette before starting work. Then he examines the comb on his hand-piece and changes the cutter, opens the metal door to the holding pen, stands a ewe on her hind legs and walks her out. She nestles easily between his legs and he bends double over her head to shave her tail.

Adrian machine-shearing

Ama Bolton, poet and felt-maker, is in the clutter of her simple kitchen, making one of her felt foraging baskets. She tears and pats the wool on her scrubbed pine table, puddling it with water and olive oil soap.

'I got this fleece from Chris Sully on the Quantocks, it's Zwartbles, he said I should come and take them away, he was going to burn them, he doesn't get anything like as much for coloured fleeces. It's a lovely colour, the younger they are the blacker they are, they go browner with age. It felts quite easily.'

She lays on the swirly pattern, silvery wool from a Wensleydale, stroking and lathering her mat of fibres. As she works she sweet-talks me to Mongolia where horses finish the felting, rolling it across the desert. 'My interest in felt-making goes back to the 1970s. We were in Rajastan and we wandered about in a market and on several stalls there were some very coarse felted jackets and, I thought, I must find out how this is done. I was fascinated by the seamlessness of it, the fact that you can make a garment without stitches, and you don't need a spinning wheel or loom. I like the fact I am attached to a tradition going back to prehistoric times, and people are still making it in a traditional way, in Mongolia, Kazakhstan, Uzbekistan and in the Nordic countries.'

Ama felting Zwartbles

It's been raining since May, but it's dry today. At Fernhill Farm, on the rugged Mendip hills, a couple of stout spring lambs take a run at each other. There's the thud of heads. A few fields away Andy Wear softly double-whistles to two sheepdogs and they draw some ewes from his flock of Shetlands. He pens them in, unfolds his tools and sharpens his shearing blades. 'There's quite a bit of knowledge goes into getting the blades set, the only point you ever want touching is the cutting point, keep an edge on the blades all the time, just rub the stone over them, back them off, nothing worse than trying to shear with blunt shears, gnaws at the wool.'

He catches a coffee-coloured Katmoget, hauls her onto his board and sits her up between his legs. 'It hasn't been very good weather recently for shearing, it's been showery, the bigger-coated sheep are damp. This one's a bit mucky round the back-end. Shearing gives less chance for the blowfly to lay its eggs which hatch into maggots which distress the sheep and can just eat into them and cause them to die, so it's been very challenging for the shepherd this year. Beautiful April, very hot, it also meant the blowfly season started early, combined with a mild winter, even sheep that were shorn back in early May seem to be getting fly problems now. Climate change, that's what they say. Nature's always a challenge to the shepherd, that's what makes it such an interesting way of life really.'

Andy blade-shearing on the Mendip Hills

He begins the clip. 'First its bottom and crutch, all the dirty bits, then the nearside back leg, up the backbone from the tail, step forward and up the neck and the brisket.' He spells it out as he cuts the wool, scissor-sound of blade against blade slicing through the sheep bleet. The ewe between Andy's legs is dead still. 'They don't seem to mind, I think they quite like it, being held, it's like a massage, you've got a cold steel bar running over your body, you're relaxed, and I guess after twelve months' growth of wool it must be quite nice to just feel the wind against the skin. I enjoy the blade-shearing, leaves more of a covering of wool and lanolin, there's no noise, no heat of the machine, I think the sheep quite enjoy it.'

Two-year old Kyle waddles past on his way to a large muddy puddle and stops to watch his father. 'Then, when you've joined up with the back leg, you go right down, with your left foot under the shoulder, up the back bone, they're called the long blows, then up the neck, the long blows over the back-bone, down the neck and out over the brisket.'

The sheep's brown woolly coat becomes a velvety choco-late cloak as it peels away, then the fleece is off in one piece. It's impressive. The naked ewe leaps involuntarily into the air in its new lightness. Andy shakes the fleece, folds and rolls it. 'About three kilos, enough for three big jumpers.' Then he hauls another sheep over to his board. Sheep after sheep after sheep, acquiescent partners in the arms of the shearer who runs through this ancient dance, turning and rolling them seamlessly this way and that, undressing them with his sizeable shears.

Andy blade-shearing

South Molton, on the southern fringe of Exmoor, grew rich on sheep and wool. The River Mole no longer powers its ancient woollen mills, but in a busy depot on the edge of town the wool trade is alive and kicking.

A sheet of wool is hooked up and emptied onto the slope above Brian Cottrell's counter. He is one of four wool graders at Devon and Cornwall Wools. He unfolds each fleece, tears out a tuft of wool, tugs and twists it, opens up the web of fibres, makes a judgement, then lobs it into one of the numbered bins surrounding him. 'The tuft is the staple, see this one, it's strong. If it breaks when you pull it, it's 'cast'. If the wool is matted we call it 'cott-tied' and if it has arable matter in it – straw, seeds and the like – it's 'moiety'. There are more than a hundred and fifty different grades for all the breeds and qualities. I'm grading four to five hundred fleeces an hour, more than fifteen thousand a week.'

As bins fill up they are wheeled off to be weighed and I plunge my hand into bin number 374, good sound Exmoor Horn. The wool is creamy and full of bounce. I ask Brian if his hands are soft from years of lanolin. He laughs. 'When you get further into June and July the yolk comes up in them, they get much greasier then! When I went into it I did everything and anything. I was at Wheddon Cross, the wool shed was next to the market, where the market is now. I learnt from Harry Fish and Reggie Lambert in the '60s. The farmers used to come over and ask us to check the quality of wool on the backs of their sheep then.'

Brian grading wool, South Molton

BUCKFASTLEIGH

In the nineteenth century there was a cluster of woollen mills here next to the ancient Abbey. Just one lives on. Buckfast Spinning buys native fleeces at the Bradford auctions, scours the raw wool with soft water from the river Dart, and cards, spins and dyes it. Then it is woven into carpets at its sister plant in Axminster. 'We're the only ones left in the country taking the wool from fleece to floor,' David Salter tells me.

Bales are fork-lifted into the building where a gang of six men unpack them – they come from the Devonshire moors, Welsh mountains and highlands of Scotland. Jason tears out the wool stained from the ram's raddle and other impurities, then, one at a time, feeds the matted greasy fleeces into the fierce teeth of his machine. The spikes open them up and when they are spat out the other side they have the air of rough fluff, not fleece. There's a full tub of rejected rainbow-coloured wool. 'Oh that isn't wasted, we'll put that through later, it goes into the darker shades.'

The blending has begun and the fluffy wool is now on its inexorable and noisy journey through the mill. It is drawn along streams of conveyors and pipes, swept into bins, sucked up, rolled through hot sudsy baths and doused in cold showers, huffed, puffed and blow-dried in blizzards and whizzed at speed through transparent wind tunnels. Then, soft as down, clean and white, it is compressed into bales with the force of a Titan. Even now it is still a long way from becoming yarn. This is the next transformation as man and machine card, spin, ply and dye the wool, or mix it by hand to create the Berber blends. Finally the hanks of richly coloured yarn are wound onto cones. All this, and still not one square inch of carpet.

The twister attending his bobbins of plying yarn, Buckfast Spinning Mill

The ingenious Axminster loom was developed here in the eighteenth century and gigantic automated versions of Mr. Whitty's original machine are still hard at it in the town. Axminster Carpets is a family-run carpet weaving factory and here are the skeins and cones of dyed wool yarn fresh from the Buckfast Mill – rich ginger, soft heathers, hyacinth and ocean blues, berry reds and forest greens. Richard Lawrence takes me into the commotion of looms. 'It takes six men two days to change all the colours on this loom, fourteen thousand bobbins. The pattern is in those punched holes, Jacquard cards, you've probably seen something similar in the old steam organs.' We pass under tubes of speeding yarn, guzzled up by the loom and discharged as thick-pile floral geometry. The next throws up golden runes on imperial blue, perhaps for a palace or a casino. Further on, George, a skilled weaver, patrols his loom and a roll of domestic honeysuckle carpet swells beneath the gantry. It's one of their Moorland range, woven from Exmoor and Dartmoor fleeces. We continue the tour away from the looms where machines burst open the pile of each carpet in a steam bath and the tips are sheared by a giant lawnmower.

We reach the end of the line where ordered rolls are wrapped ready for delivery. One roll is particularly cumbersome, a sumptuous red weave. 'We're having a bit of trouble moving this one, it's for Buckingham Palace, it's very deep pile, it took a brigade of Guards with scaffold poles to get the last roll of carpet we delivered into the Palace.'

In Mr. Whitty's day each elaborate seamless carpet was celebrated with a peal of bells, processed through the street and blessed before its journey. No fanfare for a roll of fine Axminster carpet today, just an echo from the past in each one.

Carpet weaving, Axminster

Christine Harvey can't remember learning to knit. 'I always could. Mother knitted, Gran knitted, so I did. When I was five, during the War, we used to knit on Friday afternoons while our teacher read us a story. Mother and Gran used to knit comforts for the troops – balaclavas, fingerless mitts, and socks – and I had the oddments, I used to knit all my own dolls' clothes, mostly in the khaki or navy! I didn't use a pattern, I've never been afraid of unpicking. We were always knitting, or doing crochet – or shelling peas. Gran used to say 'the Devil makes work for idle hands'. I do a lot of my knitting at night, I think I came from a long line of night-watchmen, I tend to sleep when the dawn chorus starts.'

Bare-foot in her little front room, a cockerel crowing in her suburban garden, Christine is knitting the back of a sweater with bamboo needles. 'This is Jacob wool from the Mendips, the fleece was mostly dark, not much white. What I did, I spun some of the blackish-brown on its own, then, with the carders, I blended some of the dark with the light, and spun that. This yarn is the two threads together, two-ply, it's what we call a marl, two tones or colours plied to make one.' The warm brindle-brown curtain of knitted wool hangs in folds from her needles and it is growing. She stops to count the rows. 'Six more, then it's the armhole shaping. I may send this one to Romania. I finished the front already, I knitted the yoke in a different wool, a white Texel I plied with Mrs. Kingcott's ginger Scotch Halfbred. I like wool. For a start it's second-hand, the sheep don't want it, they'd shed it if they weren't shorn. Then, when it's knitted and outgrown, you can unpick it and knit it up again, and, when you've worn it to death you can compost it, grow your tomatoes in it. Waste not want not.'

Christine knitting hand-spun wool

I visit The Spinners and Weavers Workshop in Staplehay on a Thursday when Olive Hampton runs her weekly workshop. Today there are eight weavers and Olive shuttles from loom to loom, untangling and tying yarn, unravelling mysteries in a soft Northern lilt.

In Lindsey's palette there are straw and pond yellows, mosses and sage. She is threading up a soft green yarn from a cheese of wool. 'Last year we had four lambs, it's our first time, they were twins or triplets from our neighbour's, Suffolks, but now they're mothers, it's so exciting. We put them with a Texel, for the meat, but next time they'll go with a ram to improve the fleece. Eventually I want to weave rugs from our own wool, so do our children, I'm here to learn how to weave, then, when we want a rug, we can weave our own.'

Linda is weaving her own cream and chocolate Jacob and Shetland fleeces and, as she lifts and lowers the shafts up and down, the treadles rattle, and she leads me on a journey around her loom. I am introduced to the heddles hanging on the shaft, the heddle horses, the shed – that magical space the pedals open up between the threads, the boat shuttle she throws through the shed, and the lamm and the raddle, old words which take us full circle, back to the field and the flock.

Hand-loom weaving in Staplehay

THE MILK

Andrew Speed and his family farm Crown Estate land on the north-facing foothills of Exmoor above the Bristol Channel. The old sandstone farmhouse is at the end of a long track, and the puddles, the sheep, and the sheepdogs who greet me, are all stained ruddy-orange from the iron in the red earth. Andrew and his wife, Tracey, have invited me to stay the night so I can be up and about at daybreak when their sheep are milked.

This is how I come to be drinking a cup of tea with Andrew at half past four the following morning, which, for me, is the dead of night. 'I remember the first time I milked a sheep, it was about twenty years ago, middle of August, I'd just got the parlour done, and had a little bucket unit, I got enough milk to fill a wine glass! People thought you were daft to be milking sheep then. When I started I just had a flock of sixty Poll Dorsets. Then David Baker's wife, Sue, came to see us, they needed some sheeps' milk to develop some new flavours of ice cream, she turned up in an old Ford Fiesta and took away some of our milk. That started our relationship. We've got a flock of up to six hundred milking ewes now, depends on the season, but we lamb and milk all year round, we milk twice a day, morning and afternoon, and our milk goes to Styles for their ice cream and to other yoghourt and cheese makers.'

We put on our wellingtons and there's now a faint viridian glow in the sky. Across the yard Thea, a local girl, is returning from the field with the flock. Andrew takes me into the milking parlour. It is dazzling. 'We've developed the Friesland cross Poll Dorset breed. You've got lots of lambs and easy lambing with the Frieslands, but they're a bit fickle, they're better in a Mediterranean climate, then you've got good lambs and lambing all year round with the Poll Dorsets. It's a good mix for milking.'

Day is just breaking. 'Pity you weren't here yesterday, the sunrise was spectacular, it's the best part of farming here, the sunrises over the sea, like Turkish Delight my youngest son says.'

Ewes going into the milking parlour at dawn

There's an old-gold crescent moon in a deep violet sky as I leave home at just gone three o'clock one June morning. By four I'm at North Wootton, north east of Glastonbury, the sky is lavender and the earth fuzzy with mist. James Bartlett is about to set off to collect the ewes from the field and as he greets me the first bird sings. 'We were milking a hundred till last week, now it's up to a hundred and forty, mostly Frieslands.' In the half-light he softly calls the scattered ewes and they stream silently from the dew-sodden field, their little udders swinging between their back legs.

In the yard they jostle to be first in line and one bangs at the metal door with her head. James laughs. 'That's Wendy, she's a Wensleydale Cross, she always rattles the door to come in.' In the fluorescent milking parlour James slides open the door and counts the first twelve in. They trot with purpose up the metal gangway, slide their heads into the yokes and tuck into their breakfast nuts. 'It's three hours milking them all, that's three hours in the morning, three hours in the afternoon, then there's all the washing down. My brother David's milking next week, we do a week on, week off.' There a rhythmic chug chug of the pump and the large glass jars fill with foamy milk. It takes fifteen minutes to milk the row then clack clack they are off down the ramp and the next twelve rush in. 'We'll be milking through the summer, till October time.'

It's seven o'clock now and sunny. James' mother, Astrid, arrives with steaming tea and flapjacks. Then she stands a churn of the new warm milk in a wheelbarrow. 'You can see it's very high tech! Hannah's making the cheese this morning, it'll be about nine o'clock when the curd sets, till then it's a bit like watching paint dry. I'll call you when it's ready,' and she sets off back through the vegetable garden to the cheese parlour with her load.

James milks the ewes

I sit and draw the lambs in the nursery pens outside and wait
for the curd to set. James fills the buckets with today's milk and
the lambs suck messily on rubber teats. 'They're with mum for
up to a month, then we train them on bottles with a mixture of
mother's milk and formula. They're out to grass at six weeks.'

It's just before nine when Astrid calls that the curd is ready
and today's cheesemaking is about to begin. I am kitted out in
white wellies and a white coat. It feels serious and it is: I've
promised not to reveal too much of what I am about to see. The
parlour is pristine and squeaky-clean, but laced with ancient
magic, a place where runny milk, with a shelf-life of days,
metamorphoses into more-ish cheese which keeps for months
and years. It's easy to overlook the mysteries in a parcel on the
delicatessen shelf.

In the parlour Hannah is kneeling on the floor brining the
last of yesterday's soft cheeses, then she picks up what looks
like a long sword and moves across to the vat of today's sloppy
warm milk which is now a huge slippery wet jelly. 'I slice the
curd into columns, it releases the whey, then I'll ladle it into the
moulds. You have to get used to the feel of it, get the balance
between science and intuition, judge how it's sinking, top up
the moulds, then you turn the trays over, twenty on a tray, there's
a technique, you lean back and turn them as you're leaning,
they're quite heavy at first, my arms used to ache when I first
started. When you turn them over for the fifth time they're a lot
lighter, the whey's draining all the time, that all goes to the pigs,
they love it. Then the cheeses are stored in the cold store, we
turn each one by hand every day – people may not realise the
work that goes into each cheese – it's a labour of love really.'

Ladling the ewes' milk curd

THE MARKET

Highbridge market is on Mondays, smack bang in the centre of town, cheek by jowl with little terraced homes and flanked by the main road and the muddy banks of the River Brue. Not for much longer: soon this traditional small fatstock market leaves for a new out-of-town site. Crisp white clouds breeze across the bright blue June sky. The yard is busy and full of plump lambs. John Booth brews tea in a large metal teapot and dishes out bacon rolls from his converted ambulance. On the blackboard there's the tally of today's entries: 1500 lambs, 50 hoggetts, 150 killing ewes and rams. It's just before eleven and the auctioneer walks through the yard ringing the traditional hand-bell. Today's trading is about to begin.

Simon farms a thousand sheep on King's Sedgemoor. 'Coming to market, it was always a tradition, not so many come now, it was always a gathering, you come to market on Monday, it's the weekly thing that you stop for, you come sometimes even if you haven't got anything to sell, you meet up, you'd miss it if you weren't here.' The congregation moves along the pens with the bidding. Some farmers stand in the pens up to their thighs in sheep. 'At one time every pen would have had somebody stood in it to show off their animals but now it's getting much rarer, not so many people stay now.'

Bidding for fat lambs, Highbridge Market

'Forty six pounds bid, six pound, six pound, six pound bid, half now, at six fifty, six eighty, seven pound, seven pound, forty seven pound, forty seven pound, going to sell them, good lamb for the money, forty seven pound, gone.' The price is settled with a slap. There are some long faces. The price has dropped from the week before.

We reach Alan, a shepherd from the hills above Bath. He is standing respectfully and expressionless in the pen with his Dorset Cross Mules. The auctioneer towers above him volleying numbers. The bidding is silent, a sleight of hand, a tip of the head. They're knocked down at £51.80 each.

'The price was good here last week. This is £1.50 less than I was hoping for, quite a lot when you've got 50. There's a boat-load of New Zealand lambs docking this week, that's why – floods the market.'

Henry in the pen, Highbridge Market

First week in July. It's raining and I'm drinking a mug of tea with John Vigar. 'We were down at seven o'clock this morning and it was pouring then. We're hoping prices are up today, they do speak of it being a bit better, it was down last week, but by the end of last week the price had come up, so I found a few more today on the strength of that. They haven't been finishing so well in this weather though.'

There are huddles of conversations. The pens are full of lambs, their wool streaked with colour. 'See those colours sprayed on their backs, the blue line, that's for a leaner carcass, the yellow is slightly fatter, for the butcher, the red's fatter again, too fat, the purple's too lean, that's a store lamb, and the orange F is 'farm assured', they make a bit more, they're all graded these days.'

The bell rings at eleven and there's sunshine and patches of ultramarine in a fast-moving sky. Paul Ashton, the Highbridge auctioneer, jumps up on the boards. There's apprehension and electricity as bidding begins. Then a palpable relief. Prices are up again. Henry Vigar is standing in the pen as their lambs are auctioned and John is pleased. 'I'm glad I brought in what I did, my 38 kilo and 39 kilo lambs made £48. I'm pleased with that.'

As I leave, sheep are being driven into lorries by men who are making odd yelping sounds and flapping their arms. The lambs are on their way.

Paul Ashton auctions fat lambs, Highbridge Market

THE ABATTOIR AND THE BUTCHER

There's a lemon light in the west as day breaks and soon there are bruised clouds on a thin blue sky. It's the tail end of the story and I am on a quest to visit the abattoir, lying as it does behind every lamb stew, woolly jumper, jar of lanolin or bonemeal for the garden. I pass a pub called the Butchers Arms and a few miles on there are silver seagulls and a liverish sea.

There's no sound of animals in the yard, just a dull hum and hiss from inside the building. A white door in a white wall opens and out steps a man in a white coat. I am nervous. This is one of the last few small family-owned abattoirs in England and Simon David takes me past the lairage, where a dozen stout lambs are easy and still in their pens. They have clean straw. 'These lambs arrived last night, they're ours, they'll go into our shops. We don't like them to be stressed, they'll know nothing about it. There are hardly any small abattoirs now, it's so much nicer for the animals if they don't have to travel too far. We've made it because Dad was so determined to keep the traditional ways.'

He goes off to scrub up and I'm kitted out in overall and hairnet. Over the next three hours I stand shoulder to shoulder with Simon and his fellow slaughtermen and witness this old hidden knowledge. I see lambs stunned in an instant, then hung, weasands tied, fleeces peeled, bodies eviscerated, entrails discarded, plucks inspected and carcasses weighed, by four men in turn. There are hooks and pullers, sharp knives and saws. Nobody speaks much, just occasionally there's a shout to duck. I step into the refrigerator with Scott, he's the runner. In here it's dead still and fifty clean carcasses are ready for the butchers shop.

The runner in the slaughterhouse

There are four huge waxy sides of beef, ten whole lambs, eleven legs, five half-lambs and five shoulders hanging in the David family's butchers shop in Minehead – it's fairly crowded! There's sawdust on the marbled floor. The counter is the worn wooden butcher's block and lying on it are two meaty breasts of chicken, a small stack of back bacon, a few lamb shanks and a noisette stuffed with apricot and black pudding. A customer asks for three lamb chops, fat ones. 'Of course, sir,' says Brian Pope with time-honoured civility. He wears a white trilby tied with royal blue ribbon. His workaday hands are robust and florid.

The shop is suddenly quiet. 'I may do some of these loins out for chops,' Brian says as he deftly snaps the ribs. Crack. 'I always liked cooking, my mother was a cook, she used to tell me all about cuts of meat. I started off on a farm in 1949, I used to spread lime on the fields, then I went on and helped a man deliver meat. I don't like the idea of not being active.' Another customer arrives. 'Would you like me to cut that edge for you, madam?' He ties the leg of lamb with string and presents it for inspection.

Nobody here wants meat that's been laundered and cling-wrapped. There are cardinal reds, cherry reds, bruised and livid reds, ruddy juicy reds, Potters pinks, plum blacks and the tangy raw smell of traditionally-hung meat.

In the butchers shop, Simon David boning lamb

THE TANNERY

I'm off my patch on an industrial estate behind Bridgwater, looking for one of only three sheepskin tanneries in the country. The wind is northerly and it's drizzling. Andrew Tinnion takes me into the gaping mouth of the cavernous Fenland tannery. We pass June working salt into fresh skins with her bare hands. 'If they're not well salted within four hours the wool falls out, there's wool-slip, and they'll felt – slivers become strings and strings become knots.'

We splash across a floor of sudsy water. Monster paddles, a century old, turn in giant drums of porridgey soup, there are miles and miles of pipes and mountainous lumps of soggy sheepskins. On the far side are two tiny silhouettes wrestling heavy wet fleeces from a thousand-gallon vat. They fling them into the air and there's a slap, slap as they land. 'Those skins have been soak-scoured. First salting, then scouring, then they're rounded, fleshed, washed and pickled – they're well and truly pickled – then dressed white or blue, fleshed again, wet-wheeled and fat-liquored. This is Malcolm, he does almost all the fleshing – five hundred skins a day – each skin eight times.' Malcolm fleshes his last skin, picks up a shovel and a fork-lift drops a new load.

Hauling soak-scoured skins in the sheepskin tannery

Martin is on the next machine along. He's wet-wheeling with pumice powder. 'It makes a nice fine nap. I've been working with sheepskins all my life, since I was 15. I wouldn't want to do anything else, there's a good camaraderie. So long as I can work here till I retire in a few years I'll be happy.' The tour continues and we pass Pete welding ancient machinery, tangerine sparks flying.

After tanning, the crust-dried skins are softened in cages, sheared, de-greased and sorted. Further on we arrive in a den of dusty cannisters piled to the ceiling. I imagine the ghost of Merlin stirring in the shadows. This is the dyeing department. There's a pair of old scales and a book full of hand-written recipes – wine, cassis, bolzano, vole, burgundy, red fox and strawberry. 'We dyed a rug for Kylie Minogue not so long ago, it's on her album cover.' We're in the here and now after all.

There are fine old machines for stretching, toggling, hooking, drying and seasoning and there's a Victorian Slocomb staker and stoner and an original gas ironing machine, it's over a hundred years old. A naked blue flame licks the metal as Nigel irons the curls out of a shocking pink fleece.

Later on, past machinists sewing coats and gloves, I walk out onto the cast-iron look-out platform. The alchemists slog below. The air smells raw and sheepy. Malcolm's fleshed skins have an eggshell sheen, there are milky rivers on the floor, tin greys, kingfisher-green aprons, a flash of lilac, frothy rhythms, the drone of dye drums. This is wizardry. These are real cauldrons. In the bowels of this building rotting animal skins are re-incarnated as furs and carpets for kings.

Malcolm fleshes sheepskins in the tannery

HAYMAKING AND THE END OF SUMMER

GLEBE FARM, PITNEY

It's the very end of July. Farmers have held their breath all through this wet summer, vainly hoping for a clear run of good weather. The grass is past its best. At last it's hot, there's a sunny sweetness in the air and the hum of tractors. Rob Walrond's meadow is a zingy lime green with a caramel blush and dusted with sugar sunshine. He's cutting it for hay. 'This is very old permanent pasture, it's not been ploughed, not for years, all natural, makes a delicate fine hay, lots of clover in it, delicious, the sheep love it. We don't cut it too early, there are rare Bee Orchids, but we should have cut it end of June. We're unbelievably late hay-making. Hopefully this dry spell will last.' By the end of Monday the cropped grass is spread over the field and toasting nicely in the sun and Rob is hopeful they can bale it on Thursday.

There's unexpected torrential rain on Thursday and Rob is miserable. 'It was almost ready last night. The clover's so delicate, it will crumble with the rain, and the grass will lose more of its goodness. There won't be a lot of good hay about this year.'

On Friday, after a damp start, it is warm and windy. Late in the afternoon Rob and his father attach the old baler to the tractor. 'We're going to give it a go, the wind's done a good job.' The mown grass is now hay, soft and strawberry-blond. Rob parts and fluffs it into rows with the wheeling machine, then the old baler thuds with a drum-beat down each ridge, gobbles it up and disgorges it gift-wrapped with pink twine – winter food parcels for the sheep. They finish baling around eight o'clock. 'It's not the end of the day yet, it's a family job now, we'll all be out this evening.' And they are. All the family – three generations – and friends, and a French student, load the traditional square bales onto the trailers well into dark. There's the age-old cheerful-ness of the harvest home in fair weather. 'I'm a lot more cheerful than I was. It's a relief when it's all in. This is all our winter feed.'

Haymaking, Pitney

Henry Fisher's lambs are grazing sea lavender, samphire and grasses, washed by the tide on the tip of a finger of land between Bridgwater Bay and the mouth of the River Parrett. There's the screech of gulls and several snowy egrets swim on a pan of brackish water. These are the salt marshes.

Henry is checking his stock. 'They go right out as far as you can see it green and way back the other side of the banks and right out on the sands.' We lurch over the sea wall in the Land-rover and drop down onto the charcoal-grey beach. 'Look you can see the tide rolling in.' Across the treacherous mud flats of the Bristol Channel, in the distance, the foamy edge of the sea is only just visible. But it is becoming sharper by the second and travelling towards us faster than a man can run, one of the highest tidal ranges in the world. We leave the beach, climb the dyke and bump back onto the salty green lawn. 'If we weren't grazing down here it would be all rough, rough grass and sea couch. English Nature, they like it grazed tight like this so the birds come in and feed.'

We circle the edge of the flock. 'You must keep your eye on them, and the tide. They can get into difficulty if the tide comes over, and there are crevices. I come down twice a day, mornings between six and seven, and then before dark in the evening. A lot of shepherding is down to observation. I'm in my seventieth year, it's a healthy life, I mean today is quite a nice day, but when you come down in the wintertime, farming down here, strong winds and that, blows everything out of the system I think.'

Grazing the salt marshes, Bridgwater Bay

It is late September and there's a big tide tomorrow. Henry is bringing the last of his ewes in off the saltings. 'I was going to take them off tomorrow but it's gale-ish and with this weather I'm not going to risk it. It floods from the Parrett right over, everything that's flat inside of this bank will be covered with water. When it's coming in it's fast, there's plenty of water out in the river, then within minutes it'll cover everything. It'll be a real boggy mess after next week. It's no place for them to be at all in the wintertime down here.'

The two sheepdogs quickly cover the ground and contain the sheep. Henry doesn't have to say much, just the odd 'bring 'em on' and then, stick in hand, he is counting them through the gate. 'Good, they're all here, none missing'.

Driving back along the track, Henry slows down to check on a field of lambs. 'I'll keep some of the ewe lambs back for breeding, they're brought up here with their mothers and they really get to know the area.' But most of the lambs have shorter lives, many have already left the farm and the remainder will soon. 'We never thought much about it really, I mean we always ate our own lamb. They're down on the saltings from May right round till September, they love it. And they're all finished on the grass. You get more flavour, a redder meat, it's a delicacy now, salt marsh lamb.'

Further on there are some good-looking Charolais and Suffolk rams in a field on the right. 'They're mine, they're biding their time, another week and I'll be putting them in with the ewes.'

Henry counting his ewes off the saltings

Glossary

CARDING

Disentangling fleece and laying fibres in same direction using hand carders or machine before spinning.

CLIP

To shear the wool (once the wool is removed from a sheep or flock it is called 'the clip').

DAGGING

Clipping away the dag-locks, the dirty locks of wool around the tail of a sheep.

FULL-MOUTH

Lambs have baby teeth into their second year, then they grow their first broad teeth and are known as 'two-tooths' (shearlings). Each year they grow two more adult teeth and then they are know as 'four-tooth', 'six-tooth', 'full mouth' – or 'broken mouth'.

HEDDLES

Parallel cords or wires in loom attached to shafts to separate warp threads, they are raised or lowered to make a shed for the shuttle to pass through.

HOGG (OR HOGGET)

A lamb in its second calendar year, still with its baby teeth. Officially, all lambs born in one calendar year become hoggs on 1st January the year following. Some farmers also use the word colloquially to refer to first-time ewe mothers up until their lambs are weaned.

KATMOGET

Shetland sheep come in a range of colours, e.g. moorit (reddy/brown) or shaela (silvery-grey), and patterns, e.g. krunet (white crown), katmoget (dark belly) and gulmoget (light underneath). Many have become rare because white wool has historically commanded better prices.

LAIRAGE

Where animals are kept calm while awaiting slaughter.

LAMM

Lever connecting treadles and shafts in a loom.

Liz Clay blends wool with hand-carders

MULE

A cross-bred sheep usually derived from a Blue-faced Leicester ram and a ewe of another breed, e.g. the Exmoor Mule is a Blue-faced Leicester ram x Exmoor Horn ewe. Generally when farmers use the word 'Mule' on its own, they are referring to the North Country Mule, i.e. a Blue-faced Leicester ram x Swaledale ewe. However, just to complicate things, a Suffolk Mule is a Suffolk ram on a North Country Mule!

PLUCK

The heart, liver and lungs.

RADDLE (FARMING)

A colouring matter, originally red ochre (but now a variety of colours), mixed to a paste and spread on the chest of a ram in sequence, so the ewes he has covered are marked with a stain for the farmer's record purposes. Some farmers now use a cake of colour fitted into a harness and strapped on the ram.

RADDLE (WEAVING)

Pegged bar (like a big wooden comb) used to separate the warp while it is wound onto the warp beam on the weaver's loom.

SCOTCH HALFBRED

Border Leicester ram crossed with a North Country Cheviot ewe.

SCOURING

Washing fleeces (with or without skin) to remove dirt and wool grease.

SHEARLING

Hoggs (mature lambs, still with their baby teeth) become shearlings when they cut their first set of broad teeth and become 'two tooths'. They are known as 'shearlings' until they get their next set of teeth, and become 'four-tooths'.

WEASAND

Gullet or throat.

Tannery process

SOAK-SCOURING

Rehydration of preserved skin; followed by fleshing, a second wash (scour) and reflesh, prior to pickling and tanning.

FLESHING A SKIN

Removal of fat and tissue from skin after soak-scouring.

PICKLING AND TANNING

The skins are soaked in acid followed by tanning agent.

FAT-LIQUORING

The last process in tanning when fat is added to allow the skins to stay supple when drying.

WET-WHEELING

Use of abrasive wheel on flesh side of tanned skin to create a smooth nap.

Scotch Halfbred with her twins

Hauling tanned fat-liquored sheepskins, Bridgwater

Paintings and Drawings

Mike Knowles slices a skin in the sheepskin workshop

Text and conversations same date as painting or drawing unless indicated otherwise
All measurements are given in centimetres
The map on page 8 is by Lyn Davies

Directory
Farms, businesses, artisans and craftspeople featured

AXMINSTER CARPETS LTD.

Family-run weaving company producing carpets using 90% British wool, including wool from its own flock of Drysdales. It owns the spinning mill and dyeing plant Buckfast Spinning Co. Ltd. Richard Lawrence is the Marketing Manger.

Axminster, Devon www.axminster-carpets.co.uk

BARTLETT BROTHERS (WOOTTON ORGANIC DAIRY)

Small mixed farm with sheep, cattle and pigs run by James and David Bartlett. Their ewes are mainly Frieslands. They produce traditional hand-made ewes' milk cheese and yoghourt which is sold through delicatessens and local farmers' markets.

Sunnyside Farm, North Wootton, Somerset т 01749 890248

AMA BOLTON

Poet, feltmaker and book-artist.

Wells, Somerset, www.amabolton.co.uk

Brining the soft cheeses, North Wootton

BUCKFAST SPINNING CO. LTD.

David Salter is the Managing Director.

Buckfastleigh, Devon (see Axminster Carpets Ltd)

LIZ CLAY

Designer-maker, felt accessories and fabric.

Wesbury-sub-Mendip, Somerset www.lizclay.co.uk

GERALD DAVID AND FAMILY, MASTER BUTCHERS

The David family own one of the few remaining small abattoirs in the country. They have several traditional butchers shops in Somerset which sell meat they slaughter themselves. They also own the Culbone Stables Inn, Porlock Hill, Somerset, which serves their own meat. Simon David is one of Gerald David's sons. Brian Pope has worked for the company since the 1980s.

www.geralddavid.co.uk

DEVON AND CORNWALL WOOLS

Grades wool from seven southern counties to international specifications. Samples are sent for testing, with results available to the trade at regular British Wool Marketing Board auctions in Bradford. Buyers bid on the quality, fineness, colour and yield of each lot. When I visited the depot Roy Webber was Manager, a wool grader for more than 30 years, 'British wool is very resilient and hard-wearing, good for carpets.'

South Molton, Devon

FENLAND SHEEPSKIN CO. LTD.

Traditional sheepskin tannery in Bridgwater, Somerset. Directors Andrew and Chris Tinnion previously worked at Morlands Tannery, Glastonbury, and started Fenland when Morlands closed in 1982. The company scour, tan and dye sheepskins and manufacture a range of sheepskin garments and other products.

Bridgwater, Somerset www.fenland-sheepskin.co.uk

FIDDLESTICKS

Barbara Sidwell opened her wool shop in 2007. She stocks a range of yarns, including British wool. She runs courses and also hosts knitting circles, which are becoming popular

ABOVE LEFT *Barbara in her wool shop (Fiddlesticks, Honiton)*
ABOVE RIGHT *Ron Fouracres rounds up sheep with his dogs*

everywhere as knitters get together to swop patterns and expertise and young people learn from older knitters.
17 New Street, Honiton, Devon www.fiddlesticksdevon.co.uk

HENRY FISHER

Henry has farmed since 1960, milking a dairy herd until 1986. He now grazes cattle (for finishing for beef) and runs a flock of mainly Suffolk Cross Mules at Salterns Farm, Steart, Somerset. In recent years he has marketed his salt marsh lamb through The Thoroughly Wild Meat Company.
www.thoroughlywildmeat.co.uk.

RON FOURACRES

Chairman of the Somerset Sheepdog Training and Trialling Club Ron has been training sheepdogs for 20 years, concentrating on improving dogs for farm work. *Glastonbury, Somerset*

OLIVE HAMPTON

Olive was spinning wool at the annual Fleece Fair at Hatch Beauchamp, near Taunton, organised by the Somerset Guild of Weavers, Spinners and Dyers. She teaches at the Spinners and Weavers Workshop in Staplehay, Taunton (see below).

CHRISTINE HARVEY

Christine has been hand-knitting all her life and has knitted for pattern publishers. She knits with wool she spins herself and other yarn. *Weston-super-Mare, Somerset*

HIGHBRIDGE LIVESTOCK MARKET, SOMERSET

Highbridge and Taunton livestock markets closed in January 2008. Business moved to the new Sedgemoor Auction Centre (Jct 24 off the M5), operated by Greenslade Taylor Hunt, where sheep sales take place three times a week. *www.gth.net*

FRANCES KEENAN

Basketmaker and peg-loom weaver. She also runs courses. *www.franceskeenan.co.uk*

MICHAEL KNOWLES (FB)

I met Michael in 2007 when he was working for a small sheepskin design company near Somerton. Card pattern pieces hung like bundles of stiff washing on the line, deconstructed hats, slippers and jackets. He weighted each pattern piece on the skin and with a tiny golden blade between thumb and forefinger cut round the template, slicing the skin like butter, 'I'm a vegetarian, but I don't have a problem with this, it's best that all the animal is used.'

ADRIAN REIERSEN

Adrian is a New Zealander, currently living in Australia. He has been shearing professionally for 18 years, half his life, and has regularly travelled the world to shear in other countries, including the UK. Several hundred shearers from New Zealand and Australia are given work visas annually by the British Government to help with the summer clip over here.

J. R. RICHARDS AND SONS

Family farm on the Exmoor coast above Porlock running a flock of prize-winning pedigree Exmoor Horn ewes and producing Exmoor Mule ewe lambs (Exmoor Horn ewe x Blue-faced Leicester ram). They also market their own Exmoor Horn lamb and mutton. (There is added colour in the form of Samuel Taylor

Coleridge, who reputedly stayed at Ash Farm, John Richards'
parents' farm, in the 18th century while writing Kubla Khan).
John Richards, Yarner Farm, Porlock Hill, Exmoor, Somerset
T 01643 862678

ANDREW SPEED

Andrew and his family run a flock of Friesland cross Poll Dorset
ewes for milk and lamb production. He milks throughout the year
and supplies ewes' milk to Styles Farmhouse Ice Cream Ltd. in the
neighbouring village and other producers of ewes' milk cheese
and yoghourt. He also has suckler cows, a few pigs, chickens and
a large acreage of cereals.

Briddicott Farm, Carhampton, Minehead, Somerset E briddicott@aol.com

SPINNERS AND WEAVERS WORKSHOP

A co-operative spinning and weaving group with its own
premises equipped with spinning wheels and looms for use
by members and students. Courses are run by Olive Hampton
and Paddy Bakker. *Sweethay Studio, Sweethay Close, Staplehay,
Taunton, Somerset T 01823 325345 or 01398 331192*

STYLES FARMHOUSE ICE CREAM LTD.

A family-run enterprise. Their range includes several ewes'
milk ice creams. They supply shops through their wholesale
business and run a fleet of ice cream vans for events. *Styles Farm,
Rodhuish, Minehead, Somerset www.styles-icecream.co.uk*

CHRIS SULLY

Ama Bolton mentioned the Zwartbles fleece Chris gave her for
feltmaking. Chris has kept rare breeds of sheep on the Quantocks
for 22 years (for meat and breeding), specialising in Dorset
Down, South Down, White-faced Woodland and other breeds,
He enjoys showing his rare breeds all over the country.

T 01823 430177

DAVE TAKLE

Dave grew up on a sheep farm locally. He sheared full-time
for fourteen years in Australia, New Zealand, America, South
Africa, the Falklands, Argentina and the UK. He now farms his

Olive Hampton spins wool at the Fleece Fair

own flock on Exmoor, teaches accredited shearing courses for British Wool Marketing Training, works as a shearer and runs shearing teams in the West Country. Some of his international friends come over to work in his shearing teams in our summer. *Zephyrs, Exton, Dulverton, Somerset T 01643 851513*

JOHN VIGAR AND FAMILY

Fourth generation family-run farm on a ridge above the Somerset Levels. Ceased dairy farming in 2000, now specialise in sheep, mainly Scotch Halfbred cross Suffolks, also beef cattle. Andrew Brooks is their full-time shepherd.
Manor Farm, High Ham, near Langport, Somerset

ROB AND LIZ WALROND AND FAMILY

Generations of the Walrond family have farmed locally. Glebe Farm is a family-run mixed organic farm with a farm shop selling their own organic free-range meat, home-grown organic vegetables and other organic produce. They hold regular farm open-days. *Pitney Farm Shop, Glebe Farm, Pitney, near Langport, Somerset www.pitneyfarmshop.co.uk*

ANDREW WEAR

Andrew grew up on a sheep farm in Somerset, sheared in Australia, and now runs a flock of Shetland sheep on the Mendips. He and his wife Jen provide camping barns, activity days and sell their home-produced lamb. Andrew also runs shearing courses for British Wool Marketing Training (hand-blade and machine shearing). *Fernhill Farm, Cheddar Road, Compton Martin, Somerset www.fernhill-farm.co.uk*

Other useful contacts

BRITISH WOOL MARKETING TRAINING LTD.

Runs a variety of Accredited Courses for the sheep producer and smallholder throughout the UK (including blade and machine shearing) *www.britishwool.org.uk*

EXMOOR FARMERS LIVESTOCK AUCTIONS

Cutcombe Market, Wheddon Cross, Somerset and Blackmoor Gate Market, Kentisbury, Devon are run by Exmoor Farmers Livestock Auctions, formed in 1997, and owned by mainly farmer shareholders in the area. *www.exmoorfarmers.co.uk*

EXMOOR HORN SHEEP BREEDERS' SOCIETY

The Society gives advice and information and encourages its members to maintain and improve standards of the breed, as well as sharing information and ideas and organising events. Pure Exmoor Horn lamb can also be purchased direct from breeders' farms through the Society website. *www.exmoorhornbreeders.co.uk*

THE KNITTING AND CROCHET GUILD

www.knitting-and-crochet-guild.org.uk

NATIONAL SHEEP ASSOCIATION

www.nationalsheep.org.uk

THE RARE BREEDS SURVIVAL TRUST

Founded in 1973 to conserve Britain's livestock heritage. *www.rbst.org.uk*

ROYAL BATH AND WEST OF ENGLAND SOCIETY

Agricultural charity founded in 1777 for the encouragement of agriculture, arts, manufacture and commerce. At the annual Royal Bath and West Show there are sheep breed championships, fleece awards, shearing competitions, wool handling and demonstrations of wool crafts and spinning. *www.bathandwest.co.uk*

SOMERSET GUILD OF WEAVERS SPINNERS AND DYERS

Events, workshops, talks and annual Fleece Fair. *www.somersetguildwsd.org.uk. (The Association of Guilds of Weavers, Spinners and Dyers www.wsd.org.uk)*

SOMERSET RURAL LIFE MUSEUM

Abbey Farm, Chilkwell Street, Glastonbury, Somerset BA6 8DB T 01458 831197
The 'Somerset Voices' archive (*www.somersetvoices.org.uk*) is available by appointment at the Museum & also at: *The Somerset Record Office, Taunton TA2 7PU T 01823 337600*

The Voices

The voices quoted were collected between 2005 and 2008. Many were recorded verbatim in notebooks at the time I was sketching. The longer quotations, however, are mostly extracts from our conversations in fields and workshops recorded by Alastair Goolden and later transcribed. During this period, Ann Heeley interviewed many of the same people for the 'Somerset Voices' archive: these interviews are available to the public (as recordings and written transcriptions) at the Somerset Rural Life Museum and the Somerset Record Office (www.somersetvoices.org.uk). I have quoted some of Rob Walrond's description of lambing from Ann's interview.

The visits to farmers are arranged chronologically according to the season, but not always in correct year order. In the catalogue of paintings and drawings there is an indication of the year in which they were made and in which the conversations and interviews took place. This might be helpful in setting the context of the visits, in particular the market conversations which took place at Highbridge Market in June and July 2007. The traditional market in Highbridge closed in January 2008 and moved to the new Sedgemoor Auction Centre.

The harvest and haymaking I witnessed at Glebe Farm, Pitney took place during the week of 30th July 2007. The Foot and Mouth outbreak was announced on the evening of 3rd August that week just as the Walrond family baled the last of their hay. The news cast its shadow over the 'the age-old cheerfulness of the harvest home in fair weather' later that night.

Postscript and Acknowledgements

Most of all I would like to pay tribute to the shepherds, farmers, artisans, craftspeople and businesses featured. You and your families and colleagues have all been incredibly encouraging, trusting and generous with your time. Thankyou.

The raw idea was to visit a few sheep farmers through the seasons and see where my sketchbook took me. Little did I think, when I dropped into the lambing shed in our village one February morning, that the journey would offer such a rich seam of images and take me as far as it did – up and down Somerset, then into Devon as I followed the wool.

There are more daily and seasonal jobs for the shepherd than I have documented, and many other people in the area whose livelihoods are connected to sheep but who are not included in this project. It was tempting to go further and, say, look for the designer on Dartmoor I'd heard of who makes felt shrouds from local fleece, visit the people marketing wool as sustainable insulation, or go on the trail of the rare breeds of sheep. There are many more stories to tell.

This book is a chronicle of my visits to just a few of the shepherds and artisans not far from my home on the Somerset Levels, a celebration of their, and our, age-old relationship with sheep.

I am indebted to sound designer Alastair Goolden and poet Mary Maher. Alastair brought his tireless enthusiasm to the project, recording our many conversations with farmers and other people as they went about their work. The project was richer for his involvement. Mary was a sounding-board from the beginning, a constructive critic and helpful editor. It has been a happy collaboration.

The following people and organisations have given invaluable assistance and advice: The Bridgwater Agricultural Society; The Royal Bath and West Society; The Lark Trust; The Elmgrant Trust; Wessex Water; Somerset County Council; South Somerset and Mendip District Councils and Taunton Deane Borough Council; Artlife; Pauline Lyle, John Richards and the Exmoor Horn Sheep Breeders' Society; Ann Heeley and the Somerset Rural Life Museum; The Exmoor National Park Authority; Paddy Bakker and the Somerset Guild of Weavers, Spinners and Dyers; Tim Martin and The Brewhouse Gallery, Taunton; Fiona Haser and New Brewery Arts, Cirencester; Nicky Knowles and Black Swan Arts, Frome; Jan Ross and The Guildhall Heritage and Arts Centre, Dulverton; Anne Read and The Museum of North Craven Life, Settle.

Special thanks to Tom Mayberry, historian, author and Somerset's Heritage Officer, for writing the foreword; Lyn Davies the book's designer; Steve Rose, who, with the printers, took care of the colour plates; Richard Sainsbury at Delmar Studio, who photographed the paintings and drawings; also many patrons, friends and my family for their advice and encouragement.

Last but not least, this project and book would have been impossible without the support of my husband, James.

Kate Lynch

Chloe and Adelaide eat Styles' ewes' milk icecream at the Low Ham Steam Rally

Ewe and lamb under the infra-red

Kate Lynch (née Armstrong) lives in Somerset with her husband, painter James Lynch. Rural working life has become a dominant theme in her paintings and drawings and has inspired community and educational art projects. This book is a sequel to *Willow – Paintings and Drawings with Somerset Voices* ISBN 0 9544394 0 6. *www.katelynch.co.uk*